THE COLLECTED

GOLD
DIGGER

VOLUME ONE, NUMBER ONE

by FRED PERRY

THE COLLECTED GOLD DIGGER vol.1, no.1, September 1994, is published by the Antarctic Press, 7272 Wurzbach Suite #204, San Antonio, Texas, 78240. Ph.#:(210) 614-0396. FAX #: (210) 614-5029. All stories and art are © 1994 Fred Perry. All other material © 1994 Antarctic Press. No similarity to any character(s) and/or place(s) is intended, and any similarity is purely coincidental.
Nothing from this book may be reproduced without the express written consent from the Antarctic Press, except for purposes of review or promotion. Print run: 3000. Printed by Brenner Printing, San Antonio, Texas.

First Printing

Written and Drawn by Fred Perry
Edited by Herb Mallette
Publisher, Back Cover copy by Ben Dunn
Cover by Fred Perry

THE END.

FIRST ISSUE COVER OF THE ORIGINAL MINI-SERIES.

BUT TELL ME, THAT IS IF YOU DON'T MIND MY ASKING, WHY HAVE YOU COME TO FIND MY FORMER HOME?

WHO ARE YOU?

DO YOU HAVE A GIRLFRIEND?

I'M THE WORLD FAM... SUPER-SCIENTIST GINA D... THIS IS MY SISTER, CH...

ARCHA... MY S... AND... TO P... DISCO... MY...

NOW I'M CONFUSED. HOW CAN GINA BE YOUR SISTER, CHEETAH?

SHE'S HUMAN YOU'RE NOT!

WELL.... ACTUALLY I'M HER FATHER'S WARD...

I WAS ORPHANED IN A WAR BETWEEN TWO DIFFERENT TRIBES OF WERE-FOLK... THE WERE-CHEETAHS AND THE WERE-WOLVES!...

"EVEN THOUGH THE SCIENCE OF THE TWENTIETH CENTURY WAS AVAILABLE TO ALL, THE BATTLES RAGED SAVAGELY WITH TOOTH AND CLAW!...

"...MAINLY BE... ONE OF TH... WAYS TO... A WERE-... IS WITH T... OR TEETH... ANOTHER...

"GINA'S FATHER WAS AN OCCULT INVESTIGATOR WHO HAD BEEN CALLED UPON TO DETERMINE THE CAUSE OF SOME HUMAN DEATHS THAT OCCURRED FROM SOME OF THE BATTLES.

"UNLIKE THE OTHER HUMANS WHO WANDERED INTO THE COMBAT ZONE, DR. DIGGERS COULD DEFEND HIMSELF AGAINST ROGUE WERE-FOLK WHO ATTACKED HIM!

"YOU SEE, GINA'S FATHER IS A SORCERER OF CONSIDERABLE POWER AND SKILL!...

"WITH THE FORMIDABLE PROTECTION OF HIS MAGICAL DEFENSES, HE PRESSED HIS INVESTIGATION UNTIL HE CAME ACROSS A GRIM SCENE.

"THE LAST OF THE WERE-FOLK FINISHED THEIR WAR, WITH BOTH SIDES DEAD AND GONE.

"HERE, THE LAST TWO WERE-CHEETAHS DEFENDED THEIR HOME AGAINST UNSURVIVABLE ODDS!

"INSIDE THEIR SMALL HOME WAS THE PRIZE THE TWO WE... CHEETAHS, BOTH HUSBAND AND... FOUGHT SO HARD TO DEFEND...

"DR. DIG... FOUND T... BABY... ME...

* IMMEDIATELY, MISS.

IS CAVERN VERY OFTEN R PEOPLE, IFE?

NOT, REALLY GINA. MY PEOPLE LIVED A SECLUDED LIFE FAR FROM THE INTERFERENCE OF OUTSIDERS.

THEN HOW COME YOU KNOW HOW TO SPEAK ENGLISH SO WELL? YOU HARDLY HAVE AN ACCENT!

MY PEOPLE HAVE STUDIED YOUR WORLD FOR A VERY LONG TIME, GINA. WE KNOW OF MANY LANGUAGES AND CULTURES FROM THE OUT-SIDE WORLD.

GINA, IF YOU DON'T STOP INTERROGATING TRIPE, I'LL PERSONALLY LASH YOUR TONGUE OUT!

STRIPE IS KIND, CONSIDERATE AND CARING! THERE'S NO NEED TO **CONFUSE** HIM WITH YOUR NIT-PICKING LITTLE QUESTIONS!

MY, MY! AREN'T WE **OVER PROTECTIVE** TODAY?!

I THINK I'LL SCOUT AHEAD TO CHECK IF THE WAY IS SAFE. I'LL CALL BACK FOR YOU IF EVERYTHING IS FINE.

BE CAREFUL, STRIPE.

OKAY CHEETAH, WHAT'S UP WITH YOU? YOU ACT LIKE YOU'VE CAUGHT THE **COOTIES** OR SOMETHING.

=sigh= ISN'T STRIPE A **DREAM**??!

I THINK I'VE FINALLY FOUND THE MAN WHO CAN MAKE AN HONEST WOMAN OUT OF ME!

YOU ALWAYS HAVE BEEN ATTRACTED TO **SCANTILY CLAD** MEN WITH ORANGE HAIR, GREEN EYES AND **TIGER STRIPES!**

HE'S GOT THE TYPE OF BODY THAT MAKES ME WANNA DO THE **WYLE-THANG!**

GREAT. NOW I'VE GOT A LOVE-SICK LYCANTHROPE ON MY HANDS!

ACRES AND ACRES OF **MEAT!**

AND HE'S MINE! **ALL MINE!** AHAHAHA!!

Hug

WHAT THIS PLACE NEEDS IS A CHANGE IN **ATTITUDE**!!

GINA! YOU **FOOL**!

THAT **GEM**! IT CAN'T **BE**!!

WHOA! THIS TRINKET DIDN'T DO THAT BEFORE... THIS PLACE MUST HAVE A HIGH CONCENTRATION OF MAGICAL ENERGY OR SOMETHING!

NEXT TIME YOU PULL A STUNT LIKE THAT, GOLD DIGGER...

...WARN ME TO PUT ON MY **SUPER NOVA** BLOCKING SHADES!

THE GEM SEEMS TO HAVE THE POWER TO REVERSE GYPHON'S **CURSE**... IF IT **WORKED** THIS TIME...

CHEETAH?

RRRR—

NEXT: "MERMAID COUNTRY"

TOP YOU'RE ABOUT OOK UMAN

TADAH! THE TOTAL PACKAGE!

LIKE WHATCHA SEE?

HEH... GINA WAS RIGHT! YOU'RE CUTE, BUT YOU'RE A SHRIMP IN YOUR HUMAN FORM.

IT'S TOO BAD YOU CAN'T SHIFT BACK TO YOUR HYBRID FORM FOR 24 HOURS.

WELL EXCUUUSE ME!

YOU'RE THE ONE WHO WANTED TO SEE HOW I LOOKED AS A HUMAN!! WHY YOU —

BE CALM, CHEETAH! STRIPE WAS MERELY JESTING.

WELL HE WASN'T VERY FUNNY, MESHA!

1 SORRY, CHEETAH. I COULDN'T ST. ANYWAY, EVERYONE HERE IS DY TO GO TO ATLANTIS WITH US.

AS ELVEN MAGIC-USERS, MY CONSORT, TARK, AND I ARE POSITIVE WE CAN HELP AGAINST THIS MYSTERIOUS WIZARD WHO ATTACKED STRIPE AND HIS PEOPLE...

STRIPE INFORMED US OF GYPHON, THE EVIL WIZARD OF ATLANTIS, WHEN HE TOLD US OF HOW HE MET YOU AND GINA. *

E ALSO TALKED OF HOW YOU D GINA RESCUED MESHA AND E FROM THE ENSLAVEMENT OF HE EVIL DRAGON, DREADWING.

I RECALL THAT YOU AND GINA WHERE SEARCHING FOR THE TIME MACHINE THAT TRANSPORTED DREADWING AND HIS LAIR OF SLAVES, IN WHICH MESHA AND I WERE CAPTIVE, FROM OUR HOME TIME AND REALM.

IF YOU HADN'T COME IN TIME TO STOP DREADWING FROM DISCOVERING THE SECRET OF THE TIME MACHINE, WHO KNOWS WHAT HAVOK HE MIGHT HAVE CAUSED!

EE GOLD DIGGER #1

THANKS FOR SAVING US, TYR. I OWE YOU ONE!

BUT WHY DID YOU RESCUE US? HOW DID YOU KNOW WE WERE HERE?

GYPHON SAID THAT HE WOULD WAGE WAR AGAINST ALL UPPER-WORLDERS AND CONQUER ALL!

WE THOUGHT ANY ENEMY OF GYPHON IS A ...POTENTIAL FRIEND OF OURS.

TELL ME, WERE YOU COMING TO DESTROY GYPHON? OR TO SURRENDER.

THAT CREEP? HMPH! CAME TO HIS BU

I'M RELIEVE TO HEAR THAT.

...FOR YOU HAD THIS IN YOUR POSSESSION!

A PRIZE MUCH TOO DANGEROUS TO SURRENDER TO GYPHON!

HEY! THAT'S THE GEM OF RETURNING!*

I USED IT TO TRACK DOWN EL DORADO... THE LOST CITY OF GOLD!*

THIS GEM HAS MANY POWERS AND INFORMATION STORED WITHIN, GINA.

THIS GEM HOLDS THE SECRETS OF MY ANCESTORS! LEGENDS, LOCATIONS OF LONG-LOST TREASURES, AND CITIES, KNOWLEDGE OVER ANCIENT POWERS, SECRETS OF THE UNIVERSE!

ONLY ONE OF GREAT POWER CAN RESIST THE TEMPTATION OF MISUSING THIS GEM'S MIGHT FOR ONE'S OWN GAIN.

WHO US? POWERFUL?? WE DIDN'T EVEN KNOW WHAT IT WAS!

BY THE WAY!... THAT GEM DOESN'T HAVE ANY TIPS FOR THINNER HIPS DOES IT?

I DON'T TH IT CAN WOR KIND OF MIF

WHAT DO YOU THINK, MESHA?

IT'S AS SHE SAYS, GINA!...

*SEE GOLD DIGGER #1 FOR DETAILS

BUT HOW ARE WE GONNA GET AWAY FROM THAT THING? WE HAVE NO **TORPEDOES** LEFT AND EVERY TIME WE **BREAK AWAY** THAT THING **CATCHES** US AGAIN!

WHAT EVER YOU ARE GOING TO DO, YOU'D BETTER DO IT **FAST**!

GET US OUTTA HERE!

I'M WORKIN' ON IT, **I'M WORKIN'** ON IT!

WAIT! I'VE GOT AN IDEA!! GET READY ON THE **MANUAL RELEASE CONTROL** FOR OUR EXTRA **FUEL CANISTERS**!

I KNO WHAT YO THINKIN IT WON WORK

I DIDN'T HEAR **YOU** GIVE ANY IDEAS, PENNY**!!**

STAND BY TO **RELEASE**...

YAAH!! WE TOO LATE, WE'RE TOO

...**NOW!** RELEASE THE **FUEL**!!...

HANG ON EVERY-BODY... I'M PUTTIN' THE **HAMMER DOWN!**

HA! HA I TOL YOU IT WORK ACE.

PENNY, I'M NOT EVEN TRYIN' TO HEAR THAT!

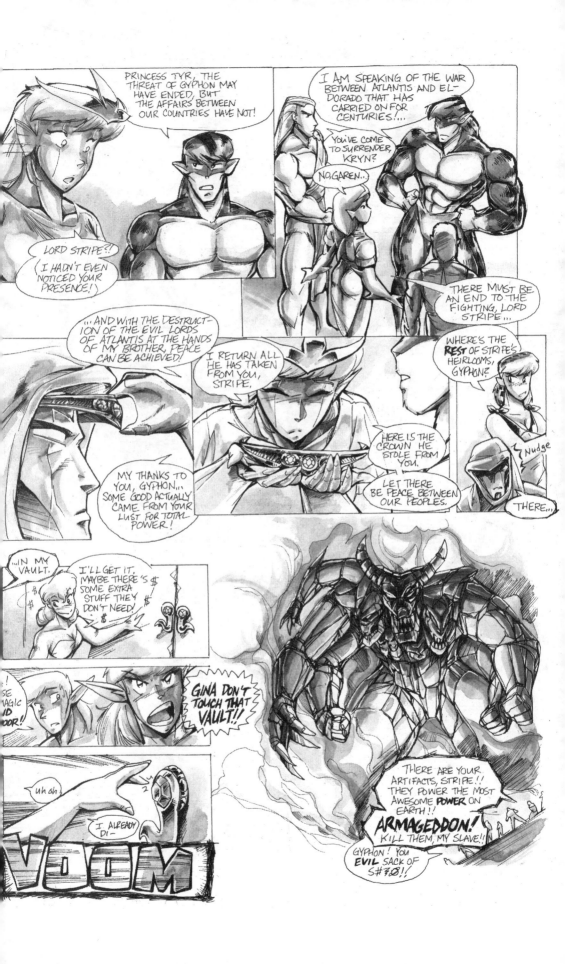

SEE GOLD DIGGER #1

THAT WHERE ALL OF ESE NEW BOOKS ME FROM?

NOPE. THEY'RE ALL FROM THE LIBRARY OF TIME IN SHANGR-LA.

I'M USING THEM TO FIGURE OUT A WAY TO STOP A RAMPAGING COLOSSUS NAMED ARMAGEDDON FROM CRUSHING THE WORLD.

OH. I GET IT ALL NOW. YOU WANT TO BE LEFT ALONE NOW, DON'T YOU?

VERY WELL... BUT I WISH YOU WOULDN'T PLAY **GAMES** WITH ME THAT WAY.

I'M NOT PLAYIN' DAD!

IT'S ALL TRUE!

U CAN GO ASK CHEETAH! HE'S DOWNSTAIRS IN THE YM WITH STRIDE, OUR FRIEND FROM EL D RADO, RIGHT NOW!...

W ARE YOUR YES, CHEETAH?*

DON'T WORRY ABOUT ME STRIPE..., MY HEALING ABILITIES CAN HANDLE A MISSING LIMB IF THEY HAVE TO...

ANYWAY..., ARE YOU READY...

NO.

GOOD!

HEETAH WAS BLINDED IN FIGHT LAST ISSUE.

GAAH!

THANKS FOR COMING DOWN AND HELPING ME WORK OUT, STRIDE.

I DON'T GET MANY CHANCES TO PRACTICE MY **JUDO THROWS** WITHOUT HOLDING BACK MY STRENGTH.

ACE VOLUNTEERED ONCE, BUT HE WOUND UP IN TRACTION FOR TWO WEEKS!

HMM... A BIT WEAK.

I'LL PUT A LITTLE MORE **UMPH** IN IT THIS TI—

NO

OoooKAY, MUFFIN... WRESTLING!!

SEE IF YOU CAN BREAK THIS HOLD!

Wha— HEY!

I THOUGHT YOU SAID YOU WERE GOING TO SHOW ME AROUND THE GYM... NOT THROW AROUND THE GYM!!

CAN'T WE DO SOMETHING WITH LESS **IMPACT**?!

AM

YOU...SHDD... NOK...FORR...YOU... ENTERR...A... RrROOM

! ?
?!

CHEE... CHEETAH??

UH OH.

STRIPE? WHATS WRONG, HONEY? PLEASE DON'T LOOK AT ME THAT WAY...

YOU... YOU'RE NOT...AFRAID OF ME, ARE YOU?

...I ...I HAD NO IDEA HOW DANGEROUS YOU CAN BECOME IF YOU LOSE YOUR TEMPER...

NO IDEA AT ALL!

STRIPE OF EL DORADO I PRESUME...

...YOU MUST ... DR. DIGGERS. ...NA'S FATHER AND ...EETAH'S GUARDIAN.

CORRECT. GINA HAS TOLD ME A LOT ABOUT YOU, MY FRIEND...

...SO YOU'RE THE YOUNG MALE WHO BRITANNY WON'T LEAVE IN PEACE THESE DAYS, HM? WELL, IF **SHE** LIKES YOU, YOU CAN'T BE SUCH A BAD FELLOW... (CAN YOU?)

I SEE. YOU ARE WORRIED THAT I MAY NOT BE RIGHT FOR HER.

IN MY HOMELAND, I WAS RAISED TO BE THE STRONGEST OF MY PEOPLE IN ORDER TO PROTECT THEM.

BEING AROUND CHEE--...(I mean) BRITANNY MAKES ME FEEL... INSUFFICIENT.

HER POWER IS TOO INTIMIDATING.

YOU MAY REST YOUR FEARS, SIR... I DON'T THINK SHE IS THE ONE FOR ME.

WHY NOT?

HMM. YOUR MIND BELIEVES WHAT YOU SAY, STRIPE... BUT YOUR **BEING** TELLS ME DIFFERENTLY.

I'M AFRAID YOU ARE USING HER EXTRAORDINARY ABILITIES AS A **SCAPEGOAT** FOR A **DEEPER** CONCERN.

TRUE, BRITANNY CAN BE TERRIBLY INTIMIDATING, BUT YOU CAN ACCEPT THAT.

YOUR TRUE **FEAR** IS IN ACCEPTING HER IN A COMMITMENT!

I DON'T CONDEMN YOUR FEARS. COMMITMENT **IS** DAUNTING, BUT LOOK WHAT YOU STAND TO GAIN FROM IT.

PERHAPS YOU ARE RIGHT. GINA SAID AS A MAGIC-USER YOU CAN READ THE AURA OF ANOTHER AND INTERPRET THE ESSENCE OF THAT PERSON. WHAT YOU SAY MUST BE TRUE.

I WILL THINK DEEPER INTO THE MATTER.

STRIPE?

'SCUSE US FOR A SEC, DAD...

LOOK... STRIPE?... I-I'M SORRY IF I—

IT WASN'T YOU OR YOUR ACTIONS CHEETAH...

I JUST NEEDED A "TIME-OUT".

I CAN SEE YOU TWO HAVE THINGS TO DISCUSS, SO I WILL LEAVE YOU IN PEACE.

BRITANNY? IF YOU NEED ME, I'M TELEPORTING TO THE LIBRARY...

AND STRIPE? I HOPE TO SEE YOU AGAIN IN THE FUTURE!

THANK YOU, DOCTOR DIGGERS. YOUR HOSPITALITY HONORS ME.

WELL I'LL BE... HE LIKES YOU! YOU TWO ACTUALLY CLICKED!!

HE D... EVEN... THE F... SKULL... ON... W...

THE FLAMING SKULL BIT: MOST FATHERS POLISH A SHOT-GUN IN FRONT OF THEIR DAUGHTER'S DATES... MY DAD MAGICALLY SETS HIS HEAD ON FIRE.

mind if I smoke?

YOU'RE THE FIRST GUY I BROUGHT TO MEET HIM WHO HE DIDN'T TRY TO INTIMIDATE!

INTERESTING.

ENOUGH ABOUT MY ADOPTED FATHER, MUFFIN...

YOU WERE VERY MEAN WHEN YOU WALKED OUT ON ME LIKE THAT!

BUT YOU CAN MAKE IT UP TO ME BY COMING TO THE GUEST ROOM WITH ME!

THE G... WITH T... WAT...

CHEETAH...

...I THINK IT'S TIME WE TOOK US SERIOUSLY.

I THINK WE BOTH SHOULD THINK THIS OUT BEFORE SOMEONE GETS HURT.

YOU... YOU DON'T LOVE ME ANYMORE, DO YOU? ≶snif≶

I UNDERSTAND. I WON'T MAKE IT HARDER THAN IT ALREADY IS. I'LL JUST TAKE MY BROKEN HEART AND CRAWL OUT OF YOUR LIFE ≶snif≶ FOREVER! ≶sob≶

DON'T OVER-REACT, CHEETAH! IT'S NOT THAT AT ALL!

THEN... IS I...

I JUST NEED MY SPACE SOMETIMES, CHEETAH. YOU SMOTHER ME TOO MUCH!

OKAY, MUFFIN. I'M FLEXIBLE...

WHAT DO YOU WANT ME TO DO?

I JUST WISH YOU WOULD'NT PAW ME WITH YOUR HANDS SO MUCH.

OKAY, MUFFIN! SEE? NO HANDS!

oh— I give up!

good!

MEANWHILE... IN THE LIBRARY OF THE DIGGERS MANSION...

Zaporozh'ye? no... Sibiu? no... Matochkin shar? no... Cleveland? maybe...

HELLO, GINA, HAVE YOU SOLVED YOUR PROBLEM YET?

ALMOST... I'M STUCK ON A MINOR DETAIL, THOUGH...

...ERHAPS I CAN HELP.

...LL, I DUNNO, ...D...

You ALWAYS BAIL ME OUT OF TROUBLE. I WANT TO DO THIS MYSELF FOR A CHANGE.

YOU WON'T BE THERE FOR ME ALL OF THE TIME YOU KNOW.

YES, BUT THIS IS A WORLD-THREATENING EMERGENCY ISN'T IT?

GOOD POINT.

ON THE TABLE HERE ARE THE TWO MAGICAL ARTIFACTS I INTEND TO USE TO STOP ARMAGEDDON AND RESCUE STRIPE'S FAMILY HEIRLOOMS THAT ARMAGEDDON DRAWS ON FOR POWER.

THE GEM OF RETURNING IS A MAGIC-NULLIFIER THAT I CAN USE TO DESTROY THE EVIL MAGIC THAT MAINTAINS ARM-AGEDDON.

THE CROWN OF THE ANCIENTS PROTECTS FROM DESTRUCTION, AND I CAN USE IT TO SAVE STRIPE'S HEIRLOOMS FROM THE EFFECTS OF THE GEM OF RETURNING.

THE PROBLEM IS... THE GEM AND THE CROWN AREN'T COMPATIBLE! IF I USE THEM AS-IS, THE CROWN 'LL PROTECT THE ARMAGEDDON FROM THE GEM, OR THE GEM 'LL BLAST STRIPE'S STUFF ALONG WITH ARMAGEDDON!

ONE OF MY BOOKS MENTIONED AN ELEMENT THAT WILL MAKE THE CROWN AND THE GEM CO-OPERATE, BUT I CAN'T FIND A SOURCE OF HINDRIUM ANYWHERE ON EARTH!

(NOT WITH THESE SURVEY MAPS ANYWAY.)

MUCH MUCH LATER... LOW OVER THE NUBIAN DESERT...

HOLDIN' STEADY AT THREE HUNDRED KNOTS AND TEN FEET, CREW...

DO WE HAVE TO FLY SO LOW, ACE?

NO, BUT ITS FUN ISN'T IT, GINA?

WHAT DO YOU THINK, CHEET

I'M NOT TALK

AW C'MON CHEETAH. YOU'RE NOT STILL MAD AT ME ARE YOU?

I'M SORRY, OKAY? PLEEASE?

WHAT'S UP WITH THOSE TWO, STRIPE?

I'M SORRY! I'M SORRY!! HMPH!

DON'T WORRY ABOUT IT, ACE.

KILL THAT NOISE! WHAT HAPPENED WHILE YOU ALL WERE AT THE MANSION, AND I WAS OUT GETTING THIS C-130 READY?...

I'VE GOT BETTER QUE

WHAT'S THAT RED, BLINKING LIGHT ON YOUR CONTROL PANEL MEAN?

WHAT?

HOLY SMOKE! SOMEONE'S GOT A MISSILE LOCK ON US!

I'D TRA M C TH B

UH-OH... RADIO MESSAGE COMIN' IN...

TANKS FA CONFOIMIN' WHO YUZ IS WIT DAT I.F.F.* CODE, ACE OLE' BUDDY-BOY!!

DARK BIRD?!!

NOW ME 'N' MY NIGHT FLIGHT KIN BLOW YUZ TA KINGDOM-SMIDDERINES!

KILL! MAIM! MASTICATE!!!

(GOOD-THING WE WERE DOIN' PICKET-DUTY HERE IN AFRICA TO PICK UP SOME EXTRA BUCKS EH, DARK BIRD?)

DAMN-STRAIGHT, BULL DOG! ITS PAY-BACK TIME!

COBR- SHUT UP, SNAKE-HEAD! YOSE AIN'T PART 'O DAT TIRED OLE UNIT NO MORE! REMEMBER??

SSORRY, DARK BIRD THISS JUST REMINDSS ME OF OLD TIMESS!

HO-BOY.

*I.F.F. (IDENTIFY, FRIEND or FOE)

LET'S SEE HOW FAST YOU ARE WITH A BROKEN SPINE, WERE-CHEETAH!

NO!

HACK-HHKEEZE!

JUST RESTRAIN HER, THABIAN!

I'M GONNA SLICE THAT YARN-BALL CHASING PIECE OF KITTY-LITTER INTO VIOLIN STRINGS MYSELF!

IN THE BUSHES...

Ughn

FIRST THAT BIG PALOOKA BREAKS MY FAVORITE GUN, THEN HE TOSSES ME INTO THE WE-- LIKE A RAG-DO--

NOW I'M MIFFED!

LUCKILY I KEEP SOMETHING HANDY JUST FOR AN EMERGENCY LIKE THIS!...

OKAY, KIBBLE BREATH, TELL CUDDLES TO LET ME GO SO WE CAN FINISH OUR FIGHT! I'M NOT AFRAID OF YOU ANYMORE!

C'MON! JUST YOU 'N' ME!

I AM SOO TEMPTED TO TAKE YOU UP ON THAT, JUST SO I CAN STOMP ON YOU SOME MORE... BUT THE FUN IS OVER... AND SO IS YOUR LIFE!

...BUT BEFORE I SEND YOU INTO THAT BIG LITTER-BOX IN THE SKY, I THOUGHT YOU MIGHT LIKE TO KNOW WHAT I HAVE IN STORE FOR YOUR COMPANIONS...

YOU KNOW... THABIAN AND I HAVE KIDS ARRIVING SOON... SO WE'LL PROBABLY NEED A NANNY...

...SO I'LL JUST INFECT YOUR HUMAN FRIEND WITH LYCANTHROPY AND SHE'LL BECOME MY OBEDIENT SLAVE AS WELL AS A DECENT, HELPFUL WERE-WOLF!

(DINNER TIME CAN BE SUCH A TRIAL IF YOU HAVE MORE THAN TWO BABIES AND NO HELP!)

NOW YOU'RE GROSSING ME OUT!

I WOULD HAVE LOVED TO HAVE YOU AS A SLAVE BUT LYCANTHROPY DOESN'T AFFECT TRUE WEREFOLK.

I WOULDN'T KNOW... I'VE HAD SHOTS FOR THAT STUFF!

THE MAN-CAT WILL SHARE YOUR FATE!

AND LIKE YOURS, HIS PELT WILL HANG IN MY DEN AS A TROPHY!

SAY YOUR PRAYERS, KITTY!

THOW   FHUSH

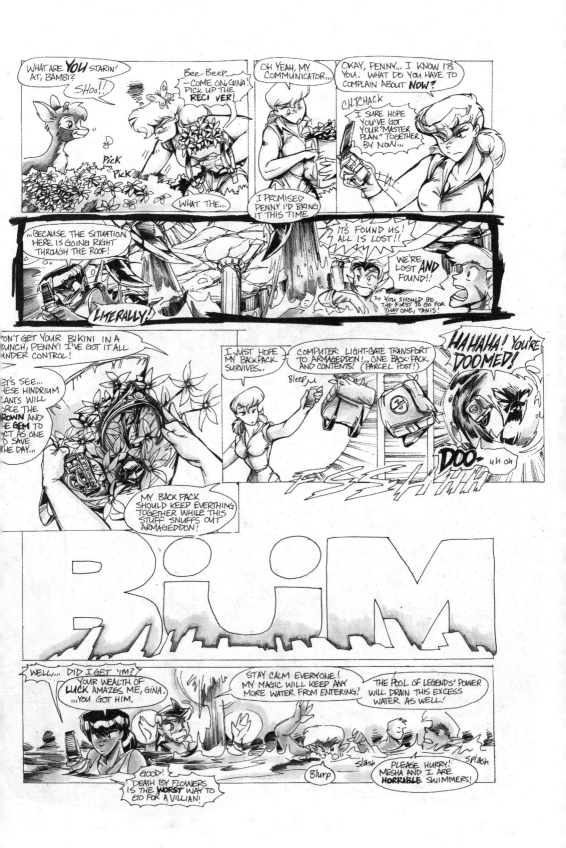

THE END.

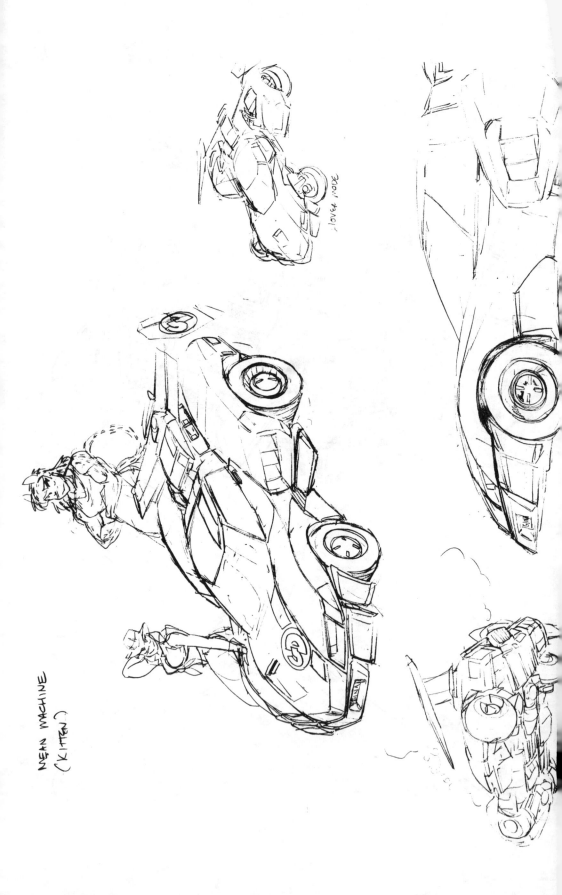

MEAN MACHINE
(KITTEN)

THE COLLECTED

GOLD
DIGGER

VOLUME ONE, NUMBER ONE

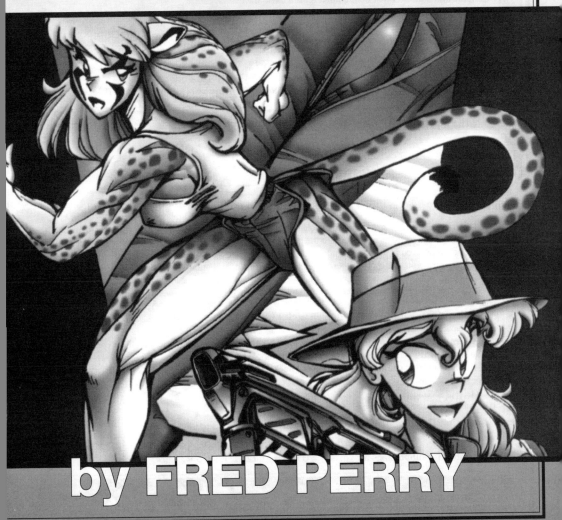

by FRED PERRY

Guidelines for Submissions

Ninja High School Yearbook '94

1. Anything in the entire **Ninja High School** Universe is fair game for a story! However, each story should contain at least one of the **NHS** characters and be fully contained. Note: due to the popularity of the three main characters you will have a better chance of being published if you feature some of the lesser-seen characters you like!) Minimum length is 1 page and the maximum is 8. There are no exceptions to these page limits. Any submissions exceeding the limits will be immediately rejected.
2. All work must be completed story and art. If you have any questions as to what is acceptable, please send us a photocopy of the work for approval before sending the actual contribution.
3. Washes and halftones are acceptable as well as zip-a-tone and other mechanical methods of shading.
4. Original art (or stats) should be on 11" x 17" board with a 10" x 15" image area (or some other proportional equivalent)
5. All stories become the property of the **Antarctic Press**, but all work will be returned. The **Antarctic Press** is not responsible for any work lost or damaged by Postal Services.
6. Payment will be a percentage of the total royalties based on sales divided between all the contributors.
7. The **Antarctic Press** reserves the right to make editorial changes of the work.
8. **Name and address must be included on the back of each page!**
9. We will not censor work, but we will not accept blatant pornography. Please be tasteful. Some sex or violence is acceptable, especially if it helps to advance the story.
10. Send submissions to: **Antarctic Press**
7272 Wurzbach Suite #204
San Antonio, TX 78240
Phone: (210) 614-0396   FAX: (210) 614-5029
11. **Deadline for submissions for the Ninja High School Yearbook '94 is September 1, 1994,** *Good Luck!*

Girls of Ninja High School

1. *Girls of Ninja High School* stories are to focus on the female character(s) of Ninja High School. Male characters may be included, but not as major characters. Note: due to the number of submissions on *Itchy* and *Asrial* stories which highlight other female characters are more likely to be published. Minimum page length is 1, maximum is 8. There are no exceptions to the page count; stories over 8 pages will be immediately rejected.
2. All work must be completed story and art. If you have any questions as to what is acceptable, please send us a photocopy of the work for approval before sending the actual contribution.
3. Washes and halftones are acceptable as well as zip-a-tone and other mechanical methods of shading.
4. Original art (or stats) should be on 11" x 17" board with a 10" x 15" image area (or some other proportional equivalent)
5. All stories become the property of the **Antarctic Press**, but all work will be returned. The **Antarctic Press** is not responsible for any work lost or damaged by Postal Services.
6. Payment will be a percentage of the total royalties based on sales divided between all the contributors.
7. The **Antarctic Press** reserves the right to make editorial changes of the work.
8. **Name and address must be included on the back of each page!**
9. We will not censor work, but we will not accept blatant pornography. Please be tasteful. Some sex or violence is acceptable, especially if it helps to advance the story.
10. Send submissions to: **Antarctic Press**
7272 Wurzbach Suite #204
San Antonio, TX 78240
Phone: (210) 614-0396   FAX: (210) 614-5029
11. **Deadline for submissions for Girls of NHS #3 is March 1, 1995.** *Good Luck!*